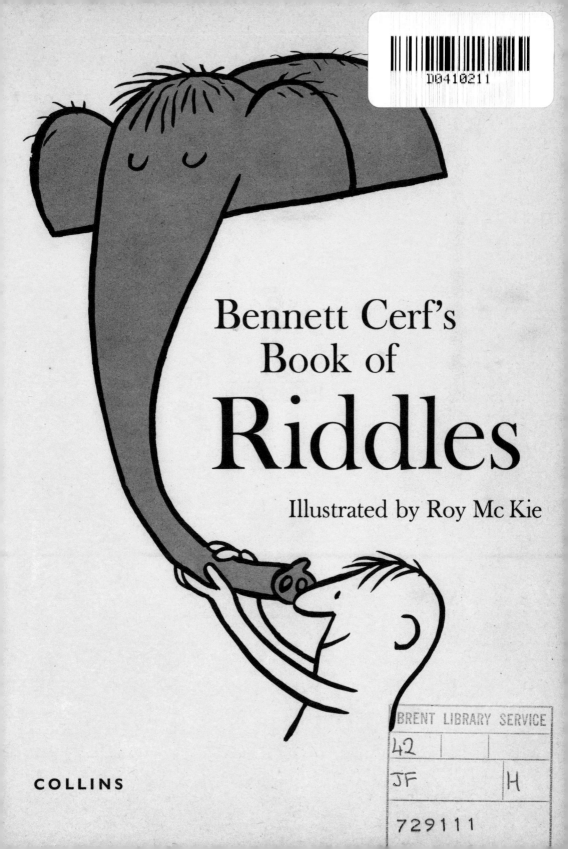

Bennett Cerf's
Book of
Riddles

Illustrated by Roy Mc Kie

COLLINS

D0410211

BRENT LIBRARY SERVICE

42		
JF		H

729111

Trademark of Random House, Inc., William Collins Sons & Co. Ltd., Authorised User

CONDITIONS OF SALE

The paperback edition of this book is sold subject to the
condition that it shall not, by way of trade or otherwise,
be lent, re-sold, hired out or otherwise circulated without
the publisher's prior consent in any form of binding or
cover other than that in which it is published and without
a similar condition including this condition being imposed
on the subsequent purchaser.

3 4 5 6 7 8 9 10

ISBN 0 00 171301 9 (paperback)
ISBN 0 00 171110 5 (hardback)

© 1960 by Bennett Cerf
A Beginner Book published by arrangement with
Random House Inc., New York, New York
First published in Great Britain 1962

Printed in Great Britain by
William Collins Sons & Co Ltd, Glasgow

Why do birds fly south?

Because it is too far to walk.

What gets lost every time you stand up?

Your lap.

What kind of dog has no tail?

A hot dog.

What is the last thing you
take off when you go to bed?

You take your feet off the floor.

What do giraffes have that
no other animals have?

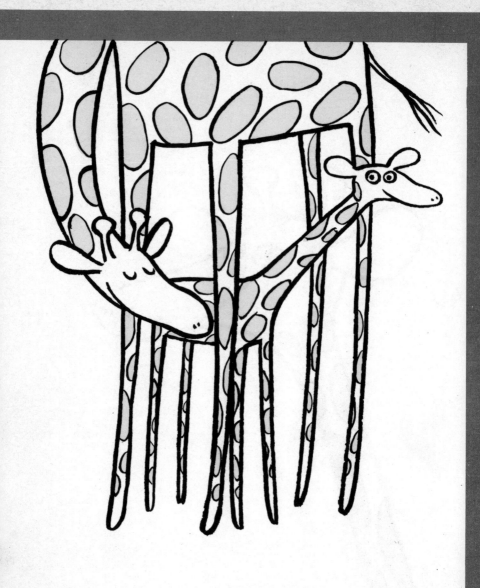

Little giraffes.

Why does the fireman wear red braces?

To keep his trousers up.

Why did the little boy throw
the clock out the window?

Because he wanted to see time fly.

What is the best way to make a fire with two sticks?

Make sure one of the sticks
is a match.

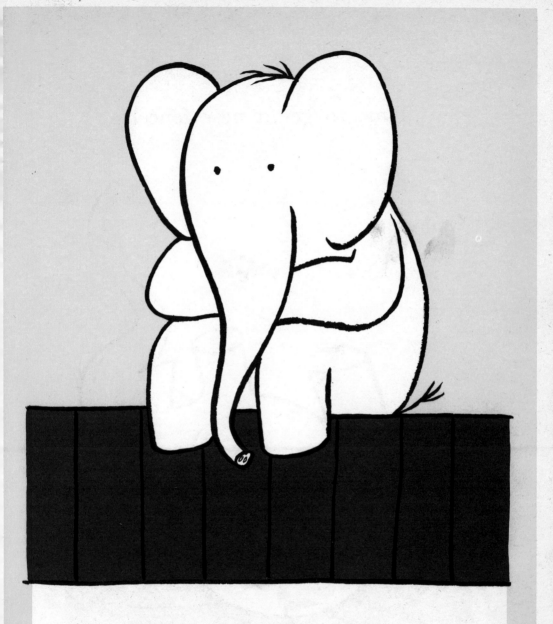

What time is it when an elephant sits on a fence?

Time to get a new fence.

What did the big firecracker
say to the little firecracker?

"My pop is bigger than your pop."

What goes up when the rain
comes down?

An umbrella.

What kind of animals can jump higher than a house?

All kinds of animals. Houses
can not jump.

What holds up a train?

Bad men.

What is a bird after he is
four days old?

Five days old.

What is the first thing you
put in a garden?

Your foot.

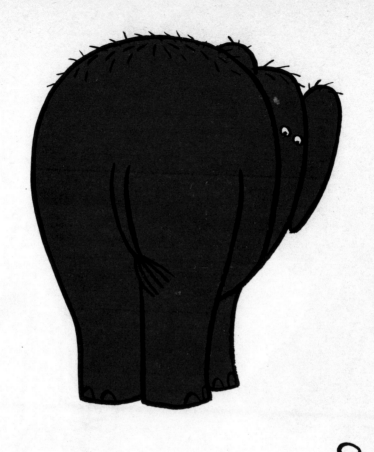

Why is an egg not like an elephant?

If you do not know, I would not want to send you to get eggs.

What dog keeps the best time?

A watch dog.

Why do white sheep eat so
much more than black sheep?

Because there are so many
more white sheep.

What is big and red and
eats rocks?

A big red rock eater.

How many lions can you
put in an empty cage?

One. After that the cage is not empty.

How many balls of string would it take to reach the moon?

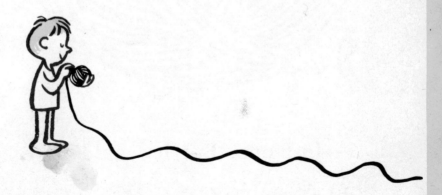

Just one. But it would have
to be a big one.

Why does a hen lay eggs?

Because if she let them drop,
they would break.

What makes more noise than
a cat stuck in a tree?

Two cats stuck in a tree.

Why does a baby pig eat so much?

To make a hog of himself.

If you drop a white hat into the Red Sea, what will it become?

Wet.

What kind of animal has a head like a cat and a tail like a cat, but is not a cat?

A kitten.

Why does a stork stand on
one leg?

Because if he took two legs off the ground, he would fall down.

Name five things that have milk in them.

Butter.

Cheese.

Ice Cream.

And two cows.

Who always goes to bed
with his shoes on?

A horse.

When is a cook bad?

When he beats an egg.

What did the pig say when
a man got him by the tail?

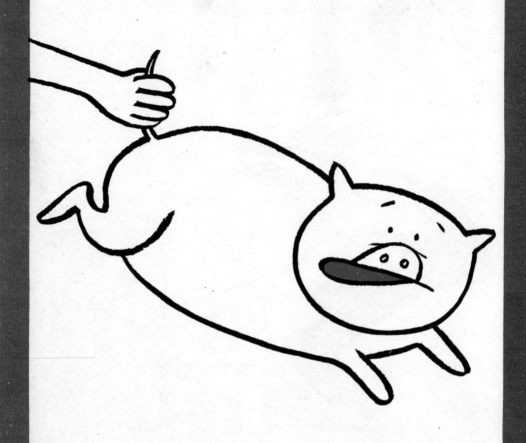

The pig said, "This is the
end of me."